BOOK TWO
TAKE UP THE FLUTE

BY GRAHAM LYONS

CHESTER MUSIC

(A division of Music Sales Limited)
8/9 Frith Street, London W1V 5TZ

TO THE STUDENT

You already know many of the tunes in this book and you will soon be able to play them all!

Do not worry if you cannot read music because, almost without knowing it, you will build up the skill as you enjoy working through the book. The **Note Recognition Games** and **Rhythm Practices** are fun to try and they will tell you how well you are doing.

Action Replays put the spotlight on potential problems. *Play these very slowly over and over again;* your fingers will quickly learn what to do and you will then be able to play them at the normal speed.

You will get a lot of fun from using this book, but remember that playing the flute is a serious business too. *Practise regularly and carefully follow the instructions of your teacher.* By doing this your playing will steadily improve and you will be able to perform even more of your favourite music.

TO THE TEACHER

The repertoire in **TAKE UP THE FLUTE** has been most carefully chosen. Each tune has a specific teaching function: it may introduce a new note or rhythm, give practice over awkward fingerings, or perhaps promote good tone production, general control and finger dexterity.

Sometimes the explanation of a new notational element is deliberately left until it has been used several times in really well known melodies. The student's aural awareness will initially carry him or her through rhythmic problems; consolidation through theory and exercises comes later.

The graded **Note Recognition Games** and **Rhythm Practices** are designed to help with note reading; there are also plenty of less familiar and original pieces for sight reading.

TAKE UP THE FLUTE is more than a 'fun' book. It provides a sympathetically structured background to each student's natural enthusiasm.

25/4/98: Practice p.1 & the Action Replays at the top of p.2.

1

STAGE 11

Assuming that you have played conscientiously through Book 1, you should now be able to play the next two pieces well enough to give yourself, and anyone listening, pleasure – which, after all, is the point of learning the instrument.

These tunes are very different from each other in mood, but they are both very popular, and both cracking good melodies. Almost certainly you will have heard them.

Practise slowly to begin with, making certain of the correct notes and rhythms.

The more difficult bits have been taken out of the tune (in the Action Replays) for separate slow and repeated practice.

THEME FROM SWAN LAKE

p mf etc. are expression marks – see page 3.

ACTION REPLAYS

 (notes with a dot on top) are called **Staccato** notes. They are held for roughly half as long as usual. A staccato crotchet would therefore be played like a quaver and a quaver rest: However, the exact length of staccato notes depends on the character of the piece they are in. For instance, in **Anitra's Dance** they should be played short and light:

ANITRA'S DANCE

E. Grieg (1843-1907)

ACTION REPLAYS

Every bar with more than one note to be practised separately – i.e:

MARKS OF EXPRESSION

p, mf, $<$, *dim.* , $>$, etc., are called **Marks of Expression**. They are abbreviations of Italian terms.

p **(piano)**	– softly	*ff* **(fortissimo)**	– extra loud
f **(forte)**	– loudly	**cresc(endo)** or $<$	– increase volume
mf **(mezzo forte)**	– half loudly	**dim(inuendo)** or $>$	– decrease volume

Italian words are also often used to indicate the speed (**tempo**) and mood of a piece. The most common ones are:-

Allegro	– quickly	**Molto**	– much
Lento	– slowly	**Ritenuto (rit)**	– slow down
Moderato	– moderately	**Andante**	– steadily
Poco	– a little	**A Tempo**	– back to the original speed

If no marks of expression are given, think what would sound best and write them in – in *pencil* (the next time you play the piece you may want to change them!).

OCTAVE PRACTICE

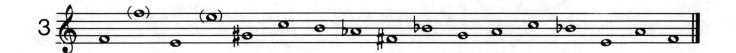

Play the first note (**F**) for a complete breath, obtaining a full, rich-sounding note. Keep your jaw loose and relaxed. Play **F** again, move your jaw forward (check in a mirror that your jaw doesn't actually go down or backwards when you think it's going forwards!), and blow the note up to the **Higher F** (up an octave). Continue the process with the remaining notes, but take frequent breaks to relieve tension: put the flute down, then waggle your wrists, breathe deeply, move your jaw, shake your head and/ or do anything else you find relaxing.

4

In No.4 breathe only where marked (V), and observe the slurs. Take fairly large breaths and keep a steady airstream going:

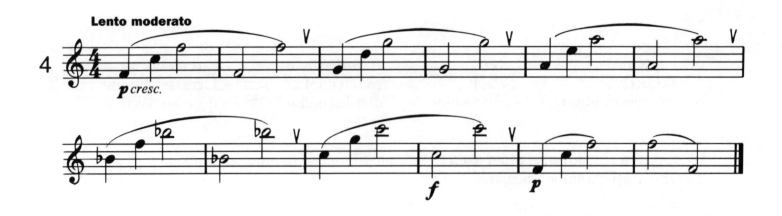

I'm sure you know the next two tunes. However, I have purposely arranged them to move suddenly from one area of the flute to the other. To go from one register to another (without hesitation) needs great flexibility. Now the enemy of flexibility is rigidity of breathing and of jaw movement. What does help, though, is to have in your head the sound of the notes you are about to play. Bear these points in mind when playing the pieces.

MY BONNIE LIES OVER THE OCEAN

H.J. Fuller

FRERE JACQUES

French trad.

6

The aim of the pieces in this Stage is to help you play confidently over a wide range. This, of course, won't happen overnight. You must practise regularly; and in that practice constantly listen to the sound you make. If any particular problem persists, check especially to see if your breathing is free and your jaw flexible. Try always to be aware of your state of tension, and if you feel tense, take a break.

ANDANTE

G.L. (1936-98?)

7

WALTZ No.3

J. Brahms (1833-97)

8

Turn over for **ACTION REPLAYS**

ACTION REPLAYS

SPANISH OCTAVES

STAGE 12
INTRODUCING SCALES AND EXPLAINING
KEY SIGNATURES

BOBBY SHAFTO in the key of C

English trad.

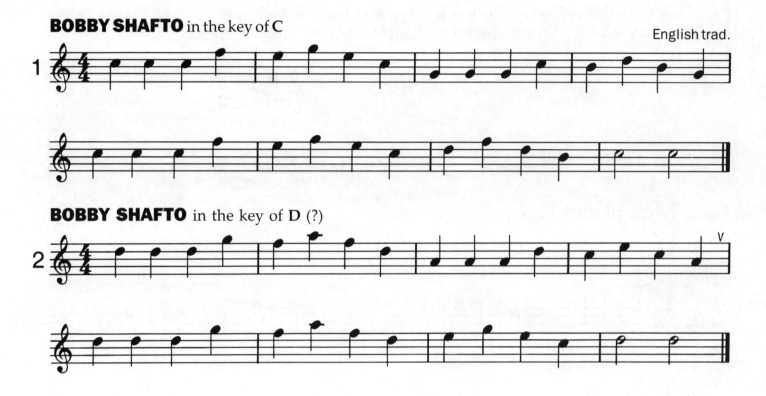

BOBBY SHAFTO in the key of D (?)

Hold on! This sounds wrong. To play **Bobby Shafto** correctly in the key of **D**, you will have to sharpen all the **F**s and **C**s:

BOBBY SHAFTO in the key of **D** (this time for real)

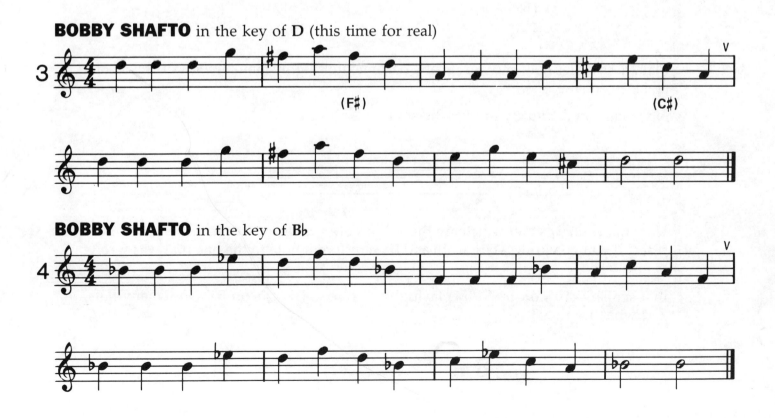

BOBBY SHAFTO in the key of B♭

In this key all the **B**s and **E**s are flattened. So – every key has its own sharps or flats which never vary. For instance:-

The key of **C** has *no sharps or flats*
The key of **G** has *one sharp*, **F♯**
The key of **D** has *two sharps*, **F♯** and **C♯**
The key of **F** has *one flat*, **B♭**
The key of **B♭** has *two flats*, **B♭** and **E♭.**

The sharps or flats that belong to a key are placed at the beginning of each stave of music and are known as the **Key Signature** of that music.

Thus the key signature of music in D is written:

and for music in B♭:

Here is the scale of **G**:

(F♯)

and the scale of **F**:

(B♭)

Play these scales over and over again: become thoroughly familiar with the *sound* of a scale. Even sing one.

Now start on **A** and try to play the scale of **A**:

How many sharps and which are they? If a note *sounds* out of place then it *is* out of place. If you go wrong, start again and try a different note to the one that was wrong before.

In a similar way, construct, by playing, the scale that starts on **B♭**. How many flats, and what are they?

Here is the first section of **God Save the Queen**, in the key of **C**:

GOD SAVE THE QUEEN

See if you are clever enough to play it starting on **D**, then **A**.

NOTE RECOGNITION GAME

These three are quite tricky and need careful thought. For 10A & B, take note of the key signature. Also check on the position of each note in the bar (is there already an accidental in front of a similar note?). 10C hasn't a key signature, but is full of notes that you are more used to calling by other names.

Time yourself how long you take to:

1. **Name** the notes.
2. **Play** the notes.

10A

10B

10C

Naming:	15 secs. – Exceptional	25 secs. – Good	35 secs. – Average
Playing:	18 secs. – Exceptional	30 secs. – Good	40 secs. – Average

However, don't be too hasty; there's a 2 second penalty for every mistake!

And now, most important: **play** each note in succession for at least 4 seconds — for tone practice, and to fix the note in your mind.

Music is written in all keys; some have as many as seven sharps or flats. So far you have only met the 'easy' keys – with few accidentals. In reality, music is no more difficult to play in one key than another; it's just a question of familiarity. To help you become more familiar with the supposedly awkward keys, here are some easy-to-play tunes. Play the first version of each tune many times, until you can play it by ear. This way you can easily check whether you are playing the tunes correctly when you attempt them in the other keys.

DOWN IN DEMERARA

Jamaican trad.

11

Down in Demerara in the key of D♭ (the flats for this key are: B♭, E♭, A♭, D♭, G♭.)

11A

Down in Demerara in the key of B (sharps are: F♯, C♯, G♯, D♯, A♯.)

11B

ANDANTE GRAZIOSO

W.A. Mozart (1756-91)

12

p dolce (sweetly)

Andante Grazioso in the key of E (sharps: F♯, C♯, G♯, D♯).

12A

Play 12A also in the higher register. Practise changing registers at will.

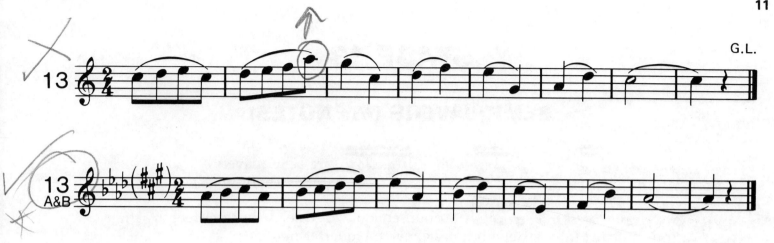

Play 13A first in the key of **A♭** (**B♭, E♭, A♭, D♭**) and then in the key of **A** (**F♯, C♯, G♯.**) The positions of the notes look the same, but you will have transposed the whole tune up a semitone. "A tune in any other key would sound the same."

RHYTHM PRACTICE (TIES)

Clap, then play:

12/9/98: Play for Anna all pieces on this page, plus CLAP one of the rhythms on p.13 (4A, 4B or 4C).

STAGE 13

SEMIQUAVERS (¹⁄₁₆ NOTES)

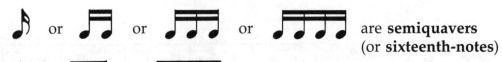

are **semiquavers** (or **sixteenth-notes**)

So four semiquavers take up the same length of time as one crotchet (four sixteenth-notes equal one quarter-note).

Here are some well known tunes with semiquavers (sixteenth-notes) in various rhythms. Don't try to work out the rhythm; play them by ear.

WHAT SHALL WE DO WITH A DRUNKEN SAILOR?

English sea shanty

1

CLEMENTINE

2

O my   dar-ling

NEW NOTE

○ ○ ○ | ○ ○ ○   E♭
(No Thumb)

C sharp

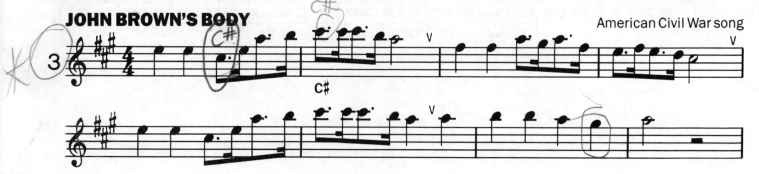

JOHN BROWN'S BODY

American Civil War song

3

C#

REMEMBER F#, C#, G#

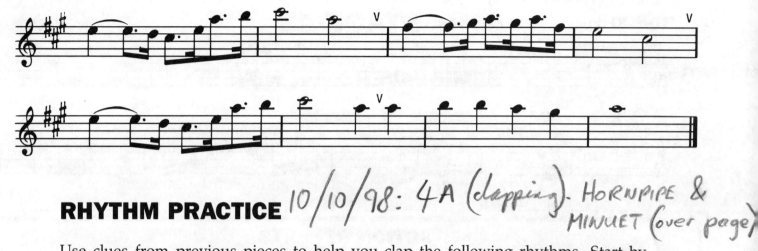

RHYTHM PRACTICE

10/10/98: 4A (clapping). HORNPIPE & MINUET (over page)

Use clues from previous pieces to help you clap the following rhythms. Start by clapping a slow, steady beat (or use a metronome at roughly 52 beats a minute):

HORNPIPE (from **The Water Music**) G.F. Handel (1685-1759)

ACTION REPLAY

14

RONDO (from **The Moor's Revenge**)   H. Purcell (1659-95)

ACTION REPLAYS

MARCHE MILITAIRE   F. Schubert (1797-1828)

ACTION REPLAY

15

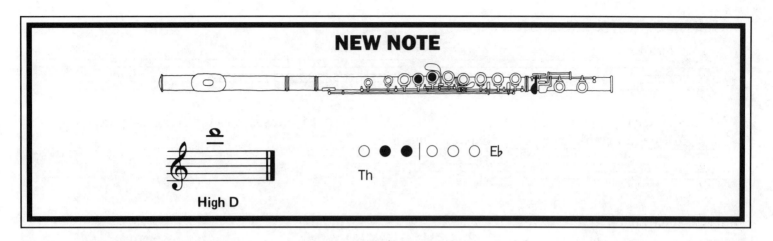

STAGE 14
COMPOUND TIME SIGNATURES

Clap a regular, slow beat for a short time and then try to make three claps take the place of each original one; *but without losing time.*

Clap each arrow:

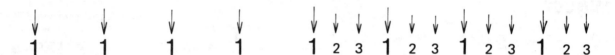

You are now clapping **Compound Time** in which each *main beat* divides into *three smaller beats.* The most usual time signature of this type is $\frac{6}{8}$; others are $\frac{3}{8}$, $\frac{9}{8}$ and $\frac{12}{8}$.

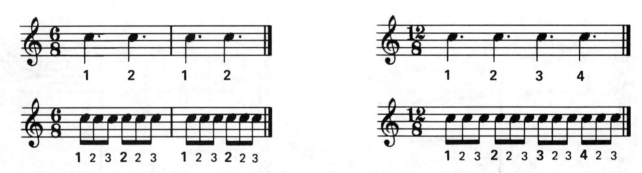

You'll notice that dotted crotchets (dotted quarter-notes), ♩. , now represent one-beat notes, while quavers (eighth-notes), ♪ , are used for the smaller beats. Each smaller beat equals one third of a main beat. ♩. = ♪♪♪

There are literally thousands of tunes in $\frac{6}{8}$ time. In fact, I don't know how I've managed to get this far with *Take Up The Flute* without using one! I'll make up for that now. Here are some of the most well known ones – you'll soon get the idea:

WHEN JOHNNY COMES MARCHING HOME

American Civil War song

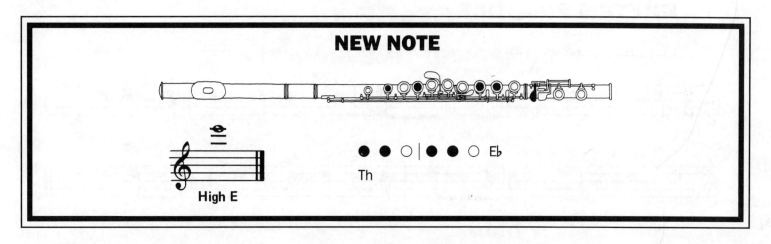

NEW NOTE

High E

Th ● ● ○ | ● ● ○ E♭

HERE WE GO ROUND THE MULBERRY BUSH

English trad.

THE IRISH WASHERWOMAN

Irish reel.

ACTION REPLAY

RHYTHM PRACTICE

Clap, then play:

Semiquavers (sixteenth-notes) fit quite logically into $\frac{6}{8}$ time, two of them taking up the same time as one quaver (eighth-note). When semiquavers (sixteenth-notes) appear in a piece in $\frac{6}{8}$ time, count each bar in 6:

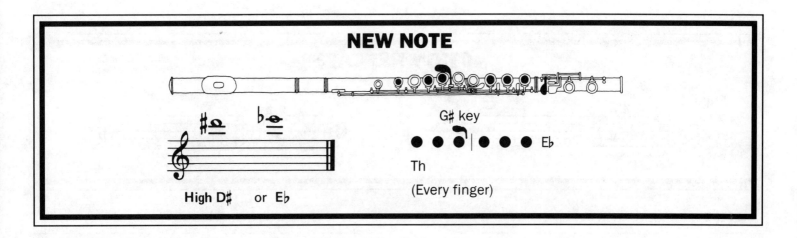

NEW NOTE

The rhythm ♩. ♫ in 6/8 time is just the same as ♩. ♪♪ in 3/4 time. Look at **Silent Night** and **The Skye Boat Song** in Stage 6 in Book 1. Here is **Silent Night** again, this time as a duet in the key of **B (F♯, C♯, G♯, D♯ and A♯)**:

Turn over for **Action Replays**

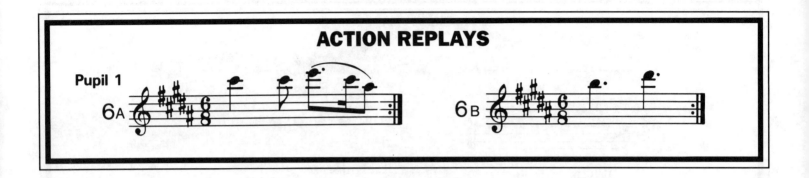

The next piece has some intricate high note work. Be sure to practise the Action Replays; make each note of the replays sound clear and play them at half speed or less.

LILLIBURLERO

Irish trad.

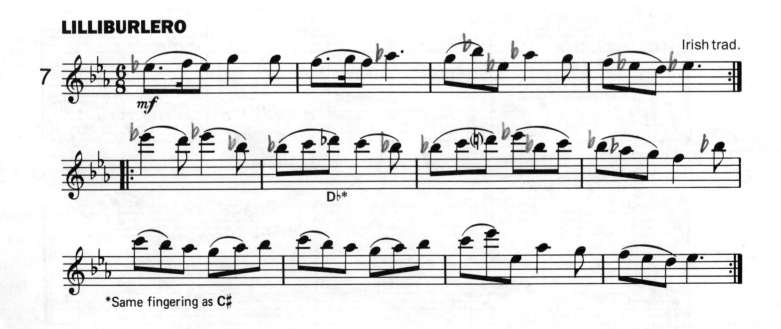

*Same fingering as C♯

ACTION REPLAYS

Pieces 8 & 9 span 250 years. They are in compound time signatures other than $\frac{6}{8}$. Exactly the same principles apply to the main and subsidiary beats.

PASSEPIED

SEND IN THE CLOWNS

S.J. Sondheim (b. 1930)

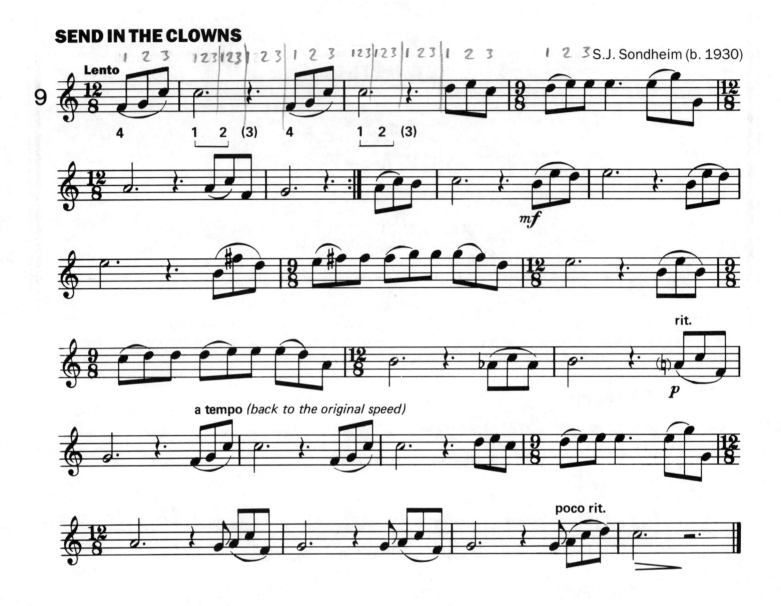

The next Stages introduce both the highest and the lowest notes on the flute; these notes will need special attention. Before you move on, consolidate by thoroughly revising the previous Stages, making sure that you have proper control of the range of notes you have learnt so far.

STAGE 15

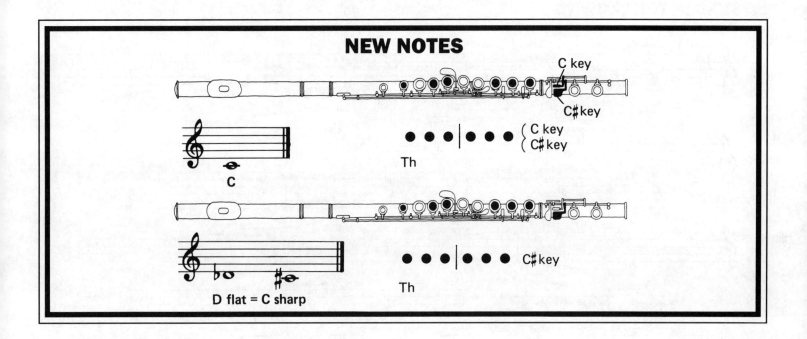

The low notes are the flute's weakest notes. You will have to give them special attention for them to match the sound of the other notes.

As you descend the scales:

1. drop the jaw back slightly, thus uncovering more of the blow hole,
2. keep the bottom lip slack,
3. direct the airstream very slightly further into the hole with the *top* lip.

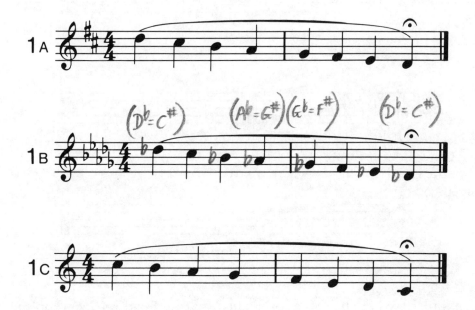

Hold the lowest note on for the remainder of your breath.

It is also not easy to produce a sound straight away on any low note. In the next exercises, keep going in a steady rhythm. If any note doesn't sound, ignore it and carry on. Notice that most of the low notes are staccato; that is, played shorter than the written value. They must be clearly separated using the tongue.

27/2/99 ✓

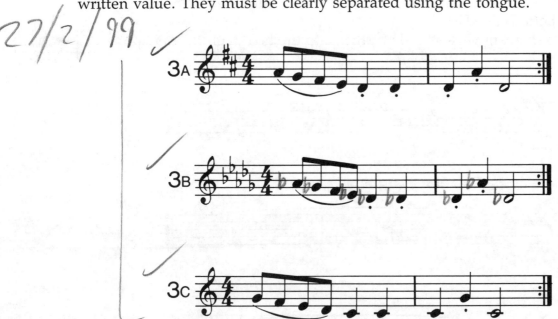

Keep alternating between the sets of exercises, bearing the three listed points in mind.

Do not practise the low notes obsessively; persuade them to come; they will not respond to force.

6/3/99

27/2/99 And now, enjoy yourself with the tunes:

CHARADE

H. Mancini (b. 1924)

Medium Waltz

expressively

CELLO THEME (from the **Unfinished Symphony**)

Schubert

 are called **triplets**.

The main beat splits into three – rather like in $\frac{6}{8}$ time.

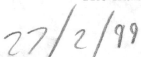

THE PINK PANTHER (hard, but fun!)

Mancini

7

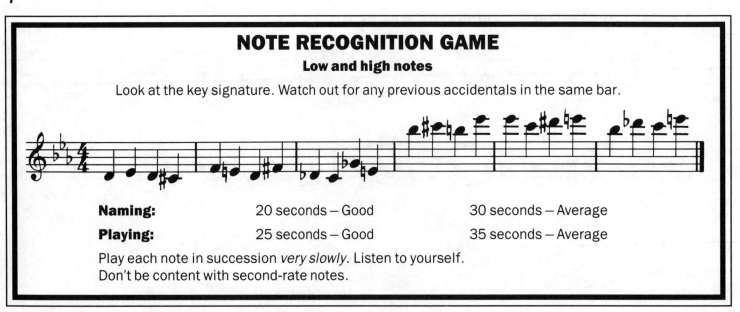

NOTE RECOGNITION GAME

Low and high notes

Look at the key signature. Watch out for any previous accidentals in the same bar.

Naming:	20 seconds – Good	30 seconds – Average
Playing:	25 seconds – Good	35 seconds – Average

Play each note in succession *very slowly*. Listen to yourself.
Don't be content with second-rate notes.

STAGE 16

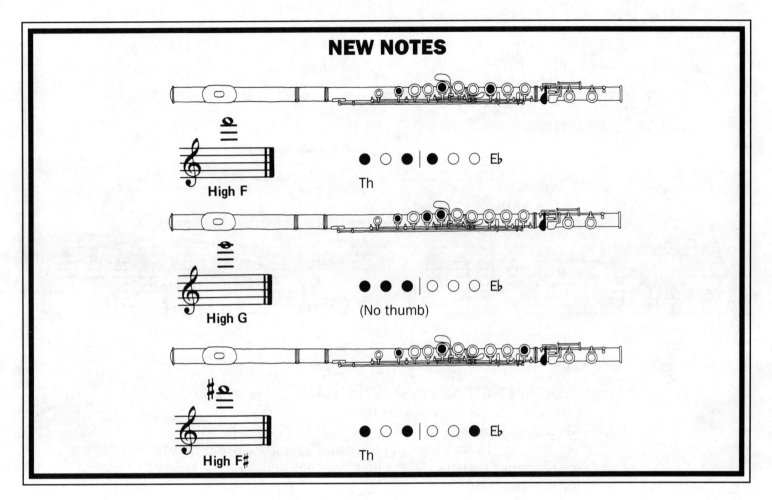

NEW NOTES

High F

High G (No thumb)

High F♯

Play a good **Middle G** (previously known as **Higher G**):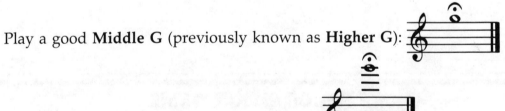

Now take your thumb off and play **High G**: This is a comparatively easy note to get. Hold on to it, and play it with the least tenseness possible. Bounce from one **G** to another:

Make up a similar exercise between these two **G**s.

Play a **High G**, and in the same breath *slur* down to **F sharp** and hold it. It may help to practise the slightly awkward change of fingering silently.

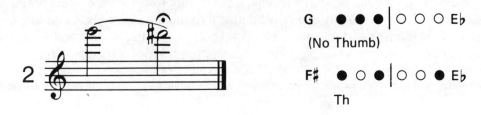

G ● ● ● | ○ ○ ○ E♭
(No Thumb)

F♯ ● ○ ● | ○ ○ ● E♭
Th

When you can play from the **G** to the **F♯** without a break, relax for a while, and, starting on the **High G**, descend through the **F♯** to **F**. Again, it helps to practise the finger movement involved separately.

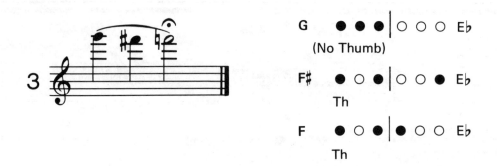

Play both scales many times, extremely slowly. Take a breath where marked.

6/3/99   6/3/99

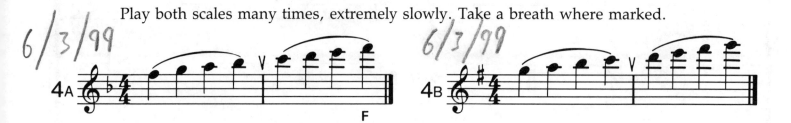

As you ascend the scale:

1. Push your jaw gradually forward, covering more of the hole.
2. Direct the airstream more upwards.
3. Keep lips relaxed.
4. Try to keep the same *quality* of sound going from the middle to the upper register. Don't imagine that you have to "reach" for the high notes.

5

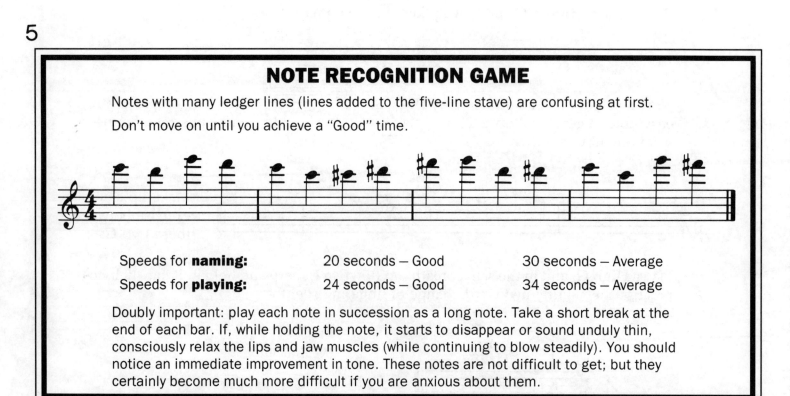

NOTE RECOGNITION GAME

Notes with many ledger lines (lines added to the five-line stave) are confusing at first.

Don't move on until you achieve a "Good" time.

Speeds for **naming:**   20 seconds – Good   30 seconds – Average

Speeds for **playing:**   24 seconds – Good   34 seconds – Average

Doubly important: play each note in succession as a long note. Take a short break at the end of each bar. If, while holding the note, it starts to disappear or sound unduly thin, consciously relax the lips and jaw muscles (while continuing to blow steadily). You should notice an immediate improvement in tone. These notes are not difficult to get; but they certainly become much more difficult if you are anxious about them.

6/3/99

BUGLE CALL (in three keys)

The next piece is difficult, but worth struggling with, as it will certainly familiarise you with the new notes:

THERE'S A HOLE IN MY BUCKET (in two keys)

English trad.

9 CORRENTE

Each player should practise his or her part separately until it is well under control. This trio should give you an indication of how much pleasure can be gained from playing the flute with others.

A. Corelli (1653-1713)

32

poco rall. 2nd time

STAGE 17
DOUBLE AND TRIPLE TONGUING

There is nothing mysterious or difficult about double or triple tonguing. For normal tonguing (**single tonguing**), one uses only the tip of the tongue, imagining the syllable "ta" (or "da" for a softer attack).

For **double tonguing**, imagine repeating the syllables "ta-ka"

ta ka ta ka ta ka ta ka

The "ka" syllable uses a part of the tongue further back. Thus with two parts of the tongue alternating it is possible to achieve greater speeds.

Groups of three notes are **triple tongued** in this way:

ta ka ta ta ka ta

Once you have the sound of these methods of tonguing in your head, they are really quite simple.

The next two themes are almost invariably played using multiple tonguing. To help you (and for a laugh), sing them to the syllables underneath, and then play them with the appropriate tonguing:

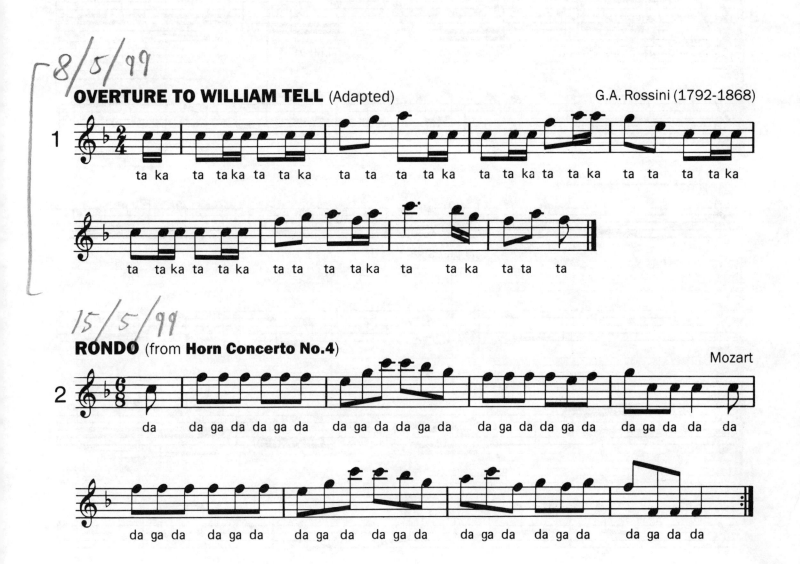

8/5/99

OVERTURE TO WILLIAM TELL (Adapted)   G.A. Rossini (1792-1868)

1

ta ka ta ta ka ta ta ka ta ta ta ta ka ta ta ka ta ta ka ta ta ta ta ka

ta ta ka ta ta ka ta ta ta ta ka ta ta ka ta ta ta

15/5/99

RONDO (from **Horn Concerto No.4**)   Mozart

2

da da ga da da ga da da ga da da ga da da ga da da ga da da ga da

da ga da da ga da da ga da da ga da da ga da da ga da da ga da da

34

SCALE OF G DOUBLE TONGUED

ta ka ta ka ta ka ta ka (similar)

SCALE OF G TRIPLE TONGUED

ta ka ta ta ka ta   (similar)

RONDO ALLA TURCA

ORNAMENTS

Musical ornaments include **Trills, Grace Notes, Turns,** in fact any alterations or additions to the bare notes to make them sound more attractive (to **ornament** them). How to play ornaments can best be learned by combining two methods:

1. Looking them up in a good music theory book (I haven't the space here to describe them).*

2. Listening sympathetically to music that contains them. You will thus develop a sense of style that will naturally guide you to their interpretation.

Trills are extremely common for the flute in all styles of music. They are produced by the rapid alternation of adjacent notes. Whether these notes are a tone or semitone apart depends on the key signature or accidentals.

The speed of a trill varies with the speed of the piece, the length of the note trilled and other factors; but above all with the capability of the player! If you can't manage a fast trill, don't try.

Trills should always be practised slowly at first, using finger muscles only.

Stop or slow down as soon as your arms or shoulders feel tense.

---

*They are particularly well covered in *The Art of Flute Playing* by Edward Putnik.

A survey of special trill fingerings is outside the scope of this book. However, trills between **C** and **D** are very common and are played using different trill keys for different octaves.

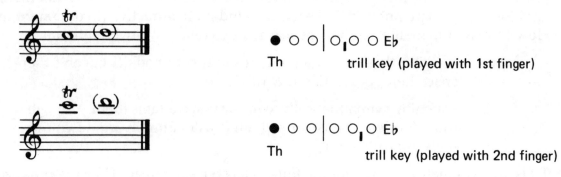

TRUMPET TUNE   Jeremiah Clarke (1670-1707)

Grace notes ♪ are extremely short, falling almost instantaneously onto the note to which they are attached: they should make that note stand out from the surrounding notes.

POLKA   Tchaikovsky

STAGE 18

It's time to talk about **tone**.

A good tone is the very basis of good flute playing.

You can only improve your tone if you have a clear idea of what good tone is. Listen to a number of professional players, in person and on record, and analyse in what essential way their playing differs from yours.

Whatever you are playing – lively pieces, sentimental tunes, exercises – always be aware of your sound.

It is best to start every practice session very simply. Play slowly descending or ascending long notes. Really listen to yourself, and try to make the flute sound as full and "liquid" as possible.

There may be occasions, when you are working hard on a new or difficult piece, when you appear to lose most of your tone and control. The reason is, almost certainly, tenseness and rigidity of breathing and jaw muscles caused by "trying too hard". The remedy is, almost certainly, to take a short break and start again with long notes and some childishly simple tune in which you can concentrate purely on tone. This will loosen you up enough to return to the piece refreshed.

The next five pieces depend upon good tone to be effective – and affecting! Some of them are known and loved all over the world. Become involved in the melodies and play them with real feeling.

8/5/99 15/5/99

JUPITER (from **The Planets**) G. Holst (1874-1934)

8/5/99

There are no bar lines in this piece: it is a free flowing folk song.

SHENANDOAH

Trad. sea shanty

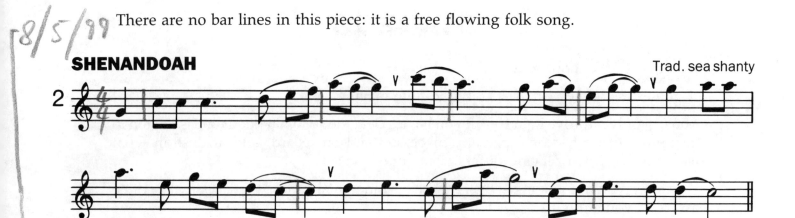

THE SUSSEX CAROL

English trad.

ALTERNATIVE B♭ KEY

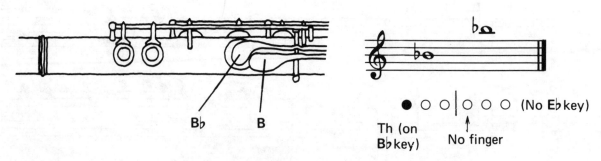

By moving your left thumb to the key on the left you can play **B flat**. With this fingering (or thumbing!), the first finger of the right hand is no longer needed. Caution: This is an alternative fingering and should only be used when pieces or particular passages contain many **B flats**. *The left thumb normally rests on the B key.*

15/5/99

Try the next two pieces using both ways of playing **B flat**:

LONDONDERRY AIR

Irish Traditional

Andante

p

poco rit. (slow down a little)

mf

f

p

THE EXILE

G.L.

Lento

mf molto espressivo

p

pp (very soft)

cresc.

mf

p

rit. (slow down)

STAGE 19

(Before attempting the high notes in this Stage, revise Stage 16. Do not play this Stage until you feel quite comfortable with all of Stage 16).

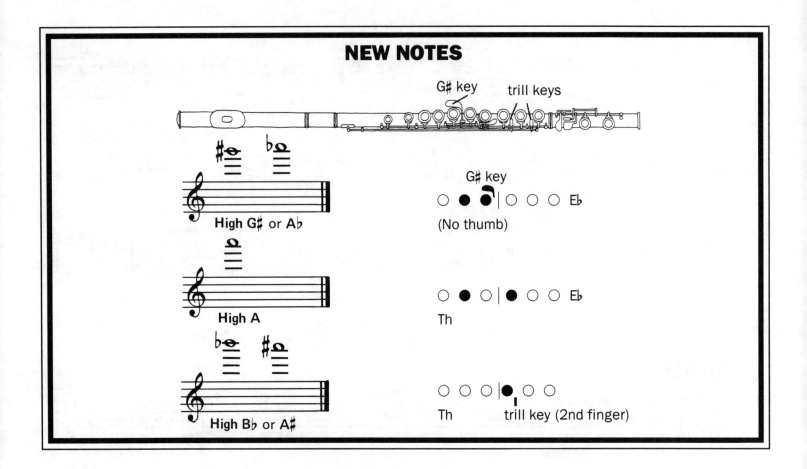

Learn these notes by first playing the same notes one octave below:

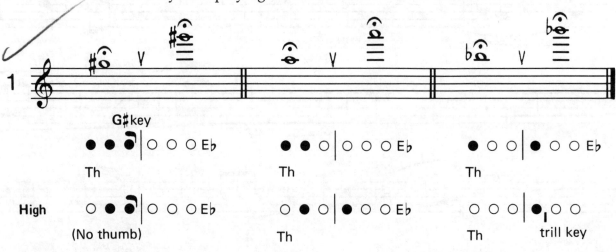

Spend about five minutes on this and then play the notes in succession, up and down, as in the next exercises:

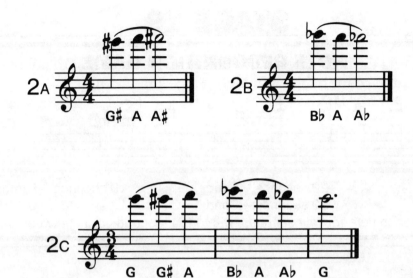

Hold on to the top note of each scale:

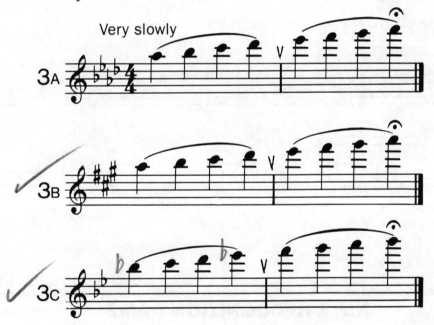

It is essential to get your mental and physical approach to playing high notes right.

Few things are more frustrating than making a feeble breathy sound instead of a note. When this happens, the temptation to increase all round mental and physical tension is almost irresistible – at least, then, you feel you are *doing* something. What you are in fact doing is forming a dangerous habit: the habit of becoming tense every time you play a high note. This habit would of course spell death to any hope of flexible, effortless flute playing. If a high note doesn't sound, it is because either you have simply not found the correct lip and jaw position, or you are not yet used to the increased breath pressure required – or most probably, a mixture of the two. Use only the muscles that are *genuinely* necessary for obtaining the notes. It is surprising how a relaxation of the jaw and facial muscles can dramatically improve the quality of the notes, although the act of relaxing feels to be the last thing that would work!

4

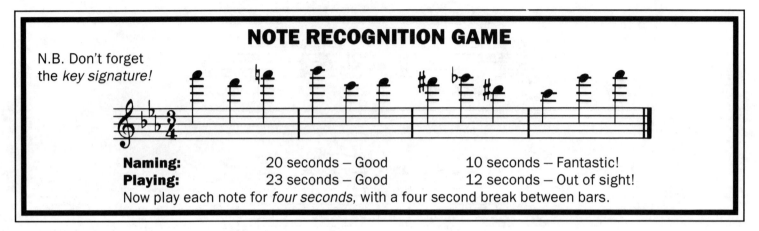

NOTE RECOGNITION GAME

N.B. Don't forget the *key signature!*

| Naming: | 20 seconds – Good | 10 seconds – Fantastic! |
| Playing: | 23 seconds – Good | 12 seconds – Out of sight! |

Now play each note for *four seconds*, with a four second break between bars.

RHYTHM PRACTICE (RESTS)

Rests are often harder to read than notes. If you have trouble with any group, substitute, temporarily, a note for a rest.

Clap, and when correct, play using **G**s in three octaves.

5

6

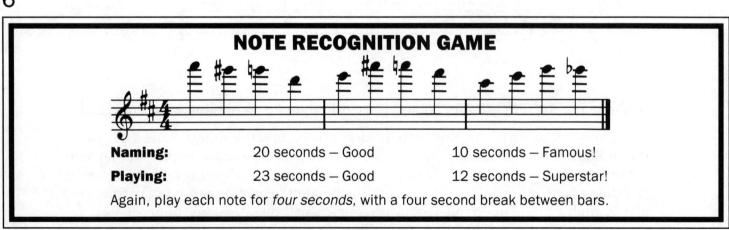

NOTE RECOGNITION GAME

| Naming: | 20 seconds – Good | 10 seconds – Famous! |
| Playing: | 23 seconds – Good | 12 seconds – Superstar! |

Again, play each note for *four seconds*, with a four second break between bars.

Before moving on to the two highest notes in the normal range of the flute, learn the next piece thoroughly. It was originally written for the flute and suits the instrument perfectly. Make each note sound full and clear, but at the same time make each section flow from beginning to end.

GAVOTTE

NEW NOTES

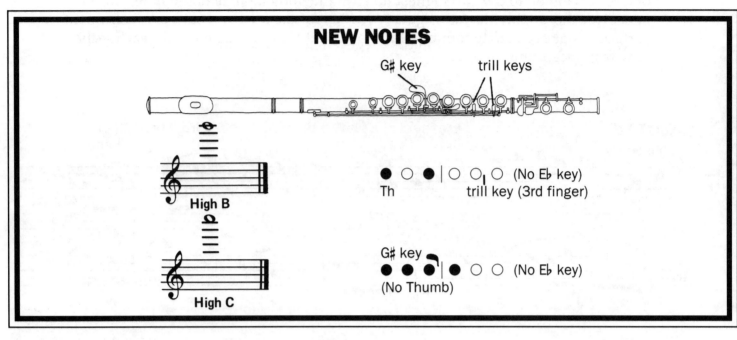

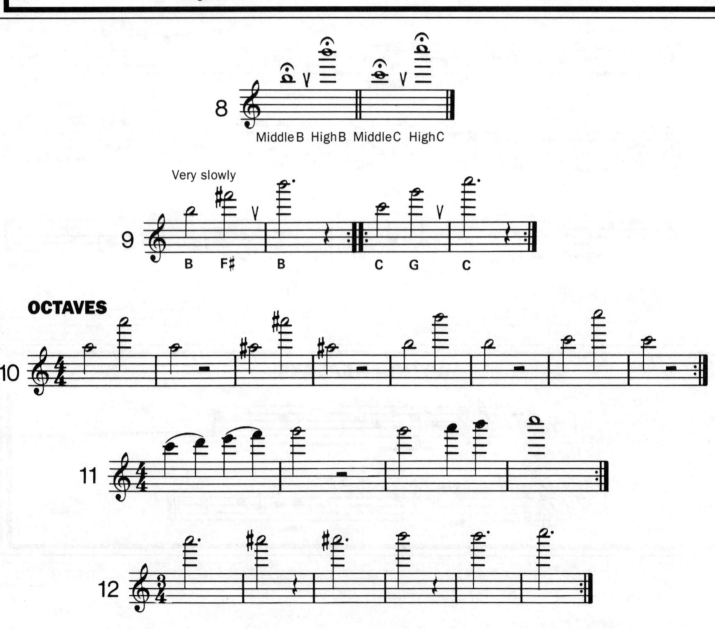

Spend no more than ten minutes on these exercises; play through the following tunes and come back to them later.

SIMPLE TUNES IN THREE OCTAVES

Play the tunes in the low and middle registers until you know them by heart. Then practise them in the top register, occasionally descending into one of the lower octaves.

High music is often written one octave lower with "8va" above it. This saves ledger lines. When the music is thereafter to be played as written, the word "loco", Italian for "place" (not "crazy"!), is used.

13 KALINKA
Russian song

14 HELAN GÅR
Old Swedish drinking song

15 SHE WAS POOR, BUT SHE WAS HONEST
(Ain't It All A Bleeding Shame)
English trad.

16 ALLEGRETTO (from the Pastoral Symphony)

Beethoven

Also play **Drunken Sailor** and **Clementine** (Nos. 1 and 2 from Stage 13, p. 12) one octave higher.

These tunes might sound simple, but playing them in the high (and sometimes the low) register certainly isn't simple. They can't possibly be learnt in one or two practice sessions.

The next Stage is entirely concerned with scale and arpeggio practice and will make you a lot more familiar with these high (and low) notes.

Try these four tunes again after you have worked over Stage 20.

STAGE 20
THE IMPORTANCE OF SCALES & ARPEGGIOS

All professional players include scales and arpeggios in their practice routines.

You have already met scales: **Arpeggios** are constructed from the 1st, 3rd & 5th notes of the scale. Thus the arpeggio of **G** uses the notes **G, B & D**, and over two octaves sounds like this:

Work out for yourself the two octave arpeggios of **D** and of **F**: using your ear if you wish, or from the relevant notes of the scale.

Classical and Romantic music, and in fact 90% of music played today, is based on the Key System. Keys are most clearly defined by their scales and arpeggios. It is therefore quite natural that most music should consist largely of scales and arpeggios in various guises. In the next well known example, you can see that much of the music is made up of the scale and arpeggio of **G**.

JESU JOY OF MAN'S DESIRING

J.S. Bach (1685-1750)

Of course, a piece of music may be in any key and may temporarily pass through different keys. It is therefore essential, if you are hoping to play the flute really well, to learn scales and arpeggios in *all* keys.

First of all, play them starting and ending on the key note (**C** for the scale of **C**; **A** for the scale of **A**). You should play all of them for two octaves.

Organise your practice this way: learn one scale and arpeggio each practice session, starting with **C** and moving up in semitones – first day, **C**, second, **D♭**, third **D**, until by the twelfth day you have covered the twelve keys. Repeat the process until you can play any scale or arpeggio by heart. This should take from four to six weeks.

When you have achieved this, practise each scale over your entire range using this all purpose scale:

The key signatures on the first stave represent the flats or sharps necessary for each scale. First play the notes as they are (no accidentals), then with 5 flats, 2 sharps and so on.

I have not written a time signature because each scale can (and should) be played in many different times and rhythms. First of all, play the notes evenly, one per beat; then with some of the following rhythms:

Invent some of your own.

The scale should be played varying the articulation, for example: all slurred, all tongued and mixtures of the two. All these ways of playing the scale are useful in themselves and make the practice more interesting.

Unfortunately there isn't an all purpose arpeggio notation: but, just the same, practise each arpeggio starting with its note that is nearest **Low C** and ending with whatever note belonging to that arpeggio is nearest **High C**. For example, the arpeggio of **A** should be practised like this:

MINOR SCALES AND ARPEGGIOS

The scales you have played are all **Major scales; Minor scales** are in two forms: **Harmonic** and **Melodic.**

Harmonic minor scales can simply be constructed flattening the 3rd & 6th note of the major scale of the same name. Compare **G major** with **G harmonic minor**:

G MAJOR

G HARMONIC MINOR

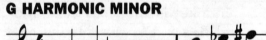

Here is **C major** scale:

C MAJOR

Write out and play **C harmonic minor:**

C HARMONIC MINOR

D MAJOR

D HARMONIC MINOR

Notice the different key signatures* and also that flattening a sharp turns it into a natural (**F♯** to **F**).

Melodic minor scales are different when going up to going down: only the 3rd is flattened going up, but the 3rd, 6th & 7th are flattened going down. This takes some learning!

G MAJOR

G MELODIC MINOR

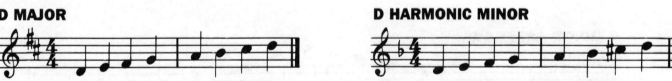

3rd   7th   6th   3rd

*This is explained on the last page.

Look at **C** and **D major scales**, then write out and play **C** and **D melodic minor scales**.

C MELODIC MINOR

D MELODIC MINOR

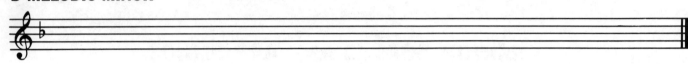

Any minor scale has the same sharps or flats in its key signature as the major scale starting a minor third above. Thus **A minor** has the same key signature as **C major, B♭ minor** the same as **D♭ major**. The major key with the same flats or sharps as a minor key is known as that minor's **relative major**. So **A minor's** relative major is C, and B♭'s is D♭. What is the relative major of **C minor, E minor, F♯ minor**? Also name the sharps or flats in their key signatures. Of course, the rules for the construction of minor scales from major ones still apply, which means that the flats or sharps in the key signature of minor scales have to be added to or altered as you play or write the scale.

Review the routine for learning the major scales and apply them to the minor scales, which should be practised in pairs, harmonic and melodic in the same practice session.

The minor arpeggio (there's only one type) is formed from the minor scale in exactly the same way as the major arpeggio from the major scale (1st, 3rd and 5th notes).

D MINOR ARPEGGIO

B MINOR ARPEGGIO

Mastering all the major and minor scales and arpeggios over the entire range of the flute is obviously a major, not a minor, undertaking. This Stage is therefore not one that you "complete". Scales and arpeggios remain an essential part of your practice for the rest of your flute-playing life.

GOOD LUCK!

COPYRIGHT ACKNOWLEDGEMENTS

FINGERING CHART

Here, for easy reference, are all the notes that you have learnt in these books.

The page numbers tell you where the notes were first introduced.

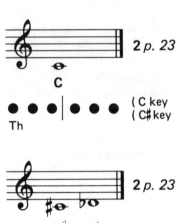

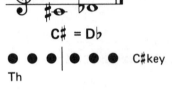

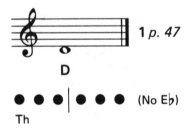

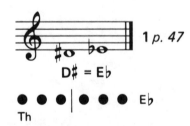

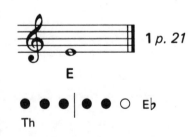

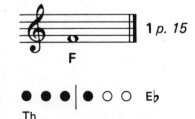

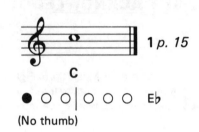

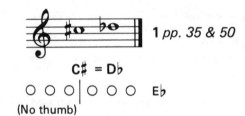

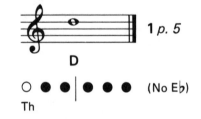

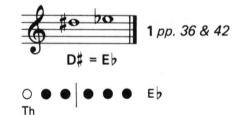

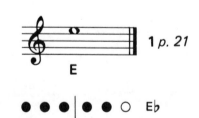

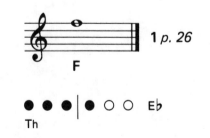

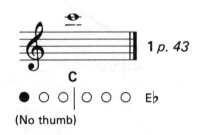

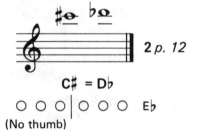

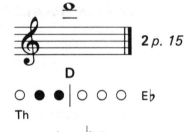

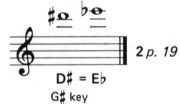

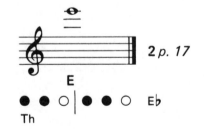

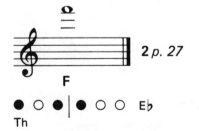

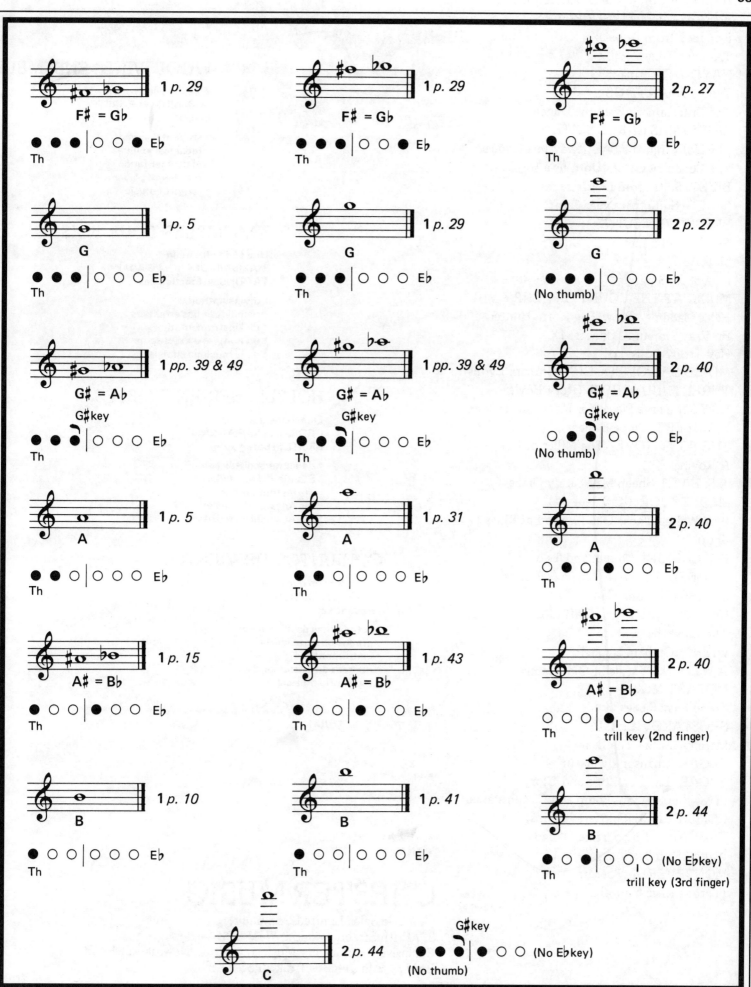

Printed by Caligraving Limited Thetford Norfolk England

11/96 (26389)

Mixed Bag

WOODWIND ENSEMBLES

A series which offers
MAXIMUM FLEXIBILITY
in relation to

* students' varied
  technical abilities
* instrumentation
* number of players
* range of music

ENSEMBLES POUR BOIS

Une série offrant un
**MAXIMUM DE CHOIX D'ADAP-
TATIONS** en fonction des

* divers aptitudes
  techniques des étudiants
* de l'instrumentation
* du nombre d'exécutants
* de la musique choisie

HOLZBLÄSER ENSEMBLES

Eine Reihe mit
**GRÖSSTER VARIATIONS-
BREITE** in bezug auf

* den unterschiedlichen
  Standard der Schüler
* die instrumentation
* die Anzahl der Spieler
* die Auswahl an Musik

CONJUNTOS DE VIENTO

Una colección que ofrece
MAXIMA FLEXIBILIDAD
en cuanto a:

* estudiantes de diferentes
  grados de experiencia
* instrumentación
* número de instrumentistas
* repertorio musical

木管アンサンブル

このシリーズは
以下の様な目的のために
最大限の適応性をもっている:

★ 生徒の様々な
  技量に応じて
★ 楽器編成に応じて
★ 演奏者の数に応じて
★ 豊富なレパートリとして

CHESTER MUSIC

(A Music Sales Limited Company)
8/9 Frith Street, London, W1V 5TZ
Exclusive distributors: Music Sales Ltd., Newmarket Road
Bury St Edmunds, Suffolk. IP33 3YB